Times Tables

Key Stage 2
For ages 7-11

Practise & Learn

Published by CGP

Editors:
Luke Antieul
Joe Brazier
Heather Gregson

With thanks to Rebecca Tate and
Stephanie Burton for the proofreading.

ISBN: 978 1 84762 745 2
Groovy website: www.cgpbooks.co.uk
Printed by Elanders Ltd, Newcastle upon Tyne
Jolly bits of clipart from CorelDRAW®

Contents

THREE times table

Here is the three times table: ➡

1	×	3	=	3
2	×	3	=	6
3	×	3	=	9
4	×	3	=	12
5	×	3	=	15
6	×	3	=	18
7	×	3	=	21
8	×	3	=	24
9	×	3	=	27
10	×	3	=	30

Practise the three times table by reading it, covering up the answers, then writing it out.

Cover up the three times table above.
Then fill in the blanks in the calculations below.

1	×	3	=	3		☐	×	3	=	18
2	×	3	=	☐		7	×	3	=	☐
☐	×	3	=	9		☐	×	3	=	24
4	×	3	=	☐		☐	×	3	=	27
☐	×	3	=	15		10	×	3	=	☐

4

Write the answers to the questions in the boxes.

What are six threes? `18`

What is three multiplied by eight? ☐

How many threes make 30? ☐

How many threes are the same as 21? ☐

What is three multiplied by five? ☐

How many threes are the same as 12? ☐

What are nine threes? ☐

How many footballs are there in each set in total?

five lots of three are ☐   five threes are ☐   5 × 3 = ☐

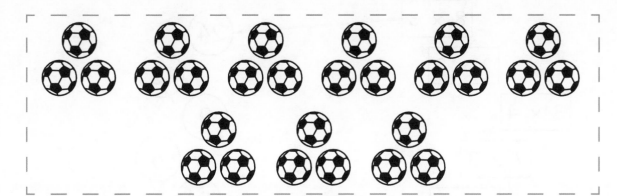

nine lots of three are ☐   nine threes are ☐   9 × 3 = ☐

THREE times table

Write the answers to the questions in the boxes.

1 A box of nails contains 10 nails. A man buys three boxes.
   How many nails does he buy?

2 Draw a line to make a path from the start to the finish.
   You can only go through the numbers in the three times table.

Start ⇨

18	3	27	8	7
17	14	9	24	11
28	2	10	15	20
16	13	19	6	32
4	25	1	21	30

⇨ Finish

3 Some friends are having a football tournament. Each team
   has eight players and there are three teams in the tournament.
   How many players are there in total?

4 Draw lines to match each multiplication to its correct answer.

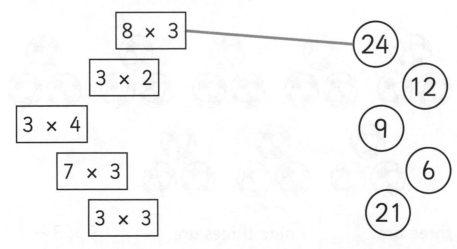

8 × 3 ——— 24

3 × 2   12

3 × 4   9

7 × 3   6

3 × 3   21

Write the answers to the questions below.
See how fast you can do them all.

5	×	3	=	15		3	×	9	=	☐
☐	×	3	=	3		3	×	☐	=	21
7	×	☐	=	21		8	×	3	=	☐
3	×	3	=	☐		3	×	7	=	☐
☐	×	3	=	18		3	×	☐	=	24
9	×	☐	=	27		9	×	3	=	☐
3	×	2	=	☐		☐	×	3	=	9
☐	×	5	=	15		☐	×	3	=	21
6	×	☐	=	18		3	×	☐	=	12
8	×	☐	=	24		3	×	1	=	☐
3	×	4	=	☐		3	×	☐	=	24
☐	×	9	=	27		10	×	☐	=	30
3	×	☐	=	24		4	×	3	=	☐
3	×	7	=	☐		☐	×	9	=	27
2	×	3	=	☐		7	×	☐	=	21
3	×	6	=	☐		8	×	3	=	☐
☐	×	3	=	27		☐	×	3	=	12
3	×	10	=	☐		☐	×	6	=	18

7

FOUR times table

Here is the four times table:

1	×	4	=	4
2	×	4	=	8
3	×	4	=	12
4	×	4	=	16
5	×	4	=	20
6	×	4	=	24
7	×	4	=	28
8	×	4	=	32
9	×	4	=	36
10	×	4	=	40

Learn the four times table.
Then test yourself by writing it out on a piece of paper.

Cover up the four times table above.
Then fill in the blanks in the calculations below.

1	×	4	=	4	6	×	4	=	☐
☐	×	4	=	8	7	×	4	=	☐
3	×	4	=	☐	☐	×	4	=	32
☐	×	4	=	16	☐	×	4	=	36
☐	×	4	=	20	10	×	4	=	☐

Write the answers to the questions in the boxes.

What is four multiplied by two? `8`

What are eight fours? ⬜

How many fours are the same as 16? ⬜

How many fours make 40? ⬜

What is four multiplied by five? ⬜

How many fours are the same as 28? ⬜

What are three fours? ⬜

How many legs are there in each set of cats and dogs?

2 dogs

$\boxed{2} \times \boxed{4} = \boxed{8}$

3 cats

$\boxed{} \times \boxed{} = \boxed{}$

4 cats

$\boxed{} \times \boxed{} = \boxed{}$

5 dogs

$\boxed{} \times \boxed{} = \boxed{}$

6 dogs

$\boxed{} \times \boxed{} = \boxed{}$

FOUR times table

The calculator multiplies each number by four.
Fill in the missing numbers.

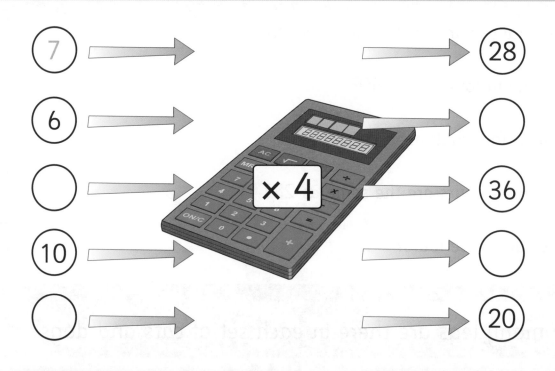

7 → → 28

6 → → ◯

◯ → → 36

10 → → ◯

◯ → → 20

Write the answers to the questions below.

1. A bag of sweets costs 9p.
   How much would 4 bags of sweets cost?
   ☐ p

2. There are 5 monkeys at a zoo. They each eat 4 bananas.
   How many bananas will the monkeys eat in total?
   ☐

3. Andy can lift 40 kg of weights. Each weight is 4 kg.
   How many weights can Andy lift?
   ☐

4. A water pistol squirts 4 litres of water each minute.
   How many litres will it squirt in 8 minutes?
   ☐ l

5. 4 people can sleep in a tent. 28 people go camping.
   How many tents will they need?
   ☐

Write the answers to the questions below.
See how fast you can do them all.

8	×	4	=	32		4	×	☐	=	12
7	×	4	=	☐		4	×	☐	=	32
4	×	☐	=	36		6	×	☐	=	24
4	×	☐	=	4		5	×	4	=	☐
☐	×	4	=	8		☐	×	4	=	36
5	×	☐	=	20		☐	×	7	=	28
4	×	☐	=	24		4	×	☐	=	16
☐	×	3	=	12		8	×	4	=	☐
4	×	7	=	☐		4	×	☐	=	20
☐	×	9	=	36		☐	×	10	=	40
1	×	4	=	☐		9	×	☐	=	36
4	×	6	=	☐		8	×	4	=	☐
10	×	☐	=	40		☐	×	4	=	16
4	×	☐	=	8		7	×	4	=	☐
5	×	4	=	☐		3	×	4	=	☐
☐	×	4	=	36		4	×	5	=	☐
4	×	☐	=	32		4	×	☐	=	32
☐	×	4	=	28		☐	×	4	=	24

Mixed Questions

Fill in the boxes to show how much
it would cost to buy these items.

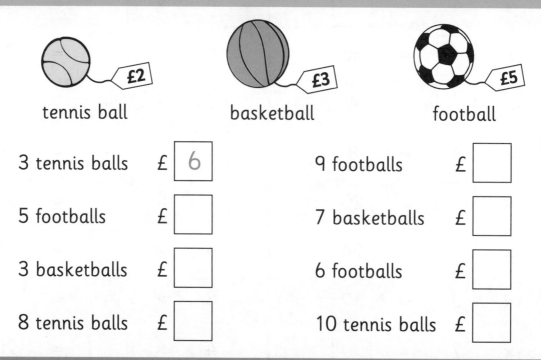

tennis ball   basketball   football

3 tennis balls   £ 6   9 footballs   £ ☐

5 footballs   £ ☐   7 basketballs   £ ☐

3 basketballs   £ ☐   6 footballs   £ ☐

8 tennis balls   £ ☐   10 tennis balls   £ ☐

Write the answers to the questions below.

1 A pig can fly a total of 7 miles in a day.
   How many miles can the pig fly in 4 days?   ☐ miles

2 Sixty sweets are divided equally into 6 piles.
   How many sweets are there in each pile?   ☐

3 It takes Bob 5 minutes to make a sandwich.
   How many sandwiches can he make in 45 minutes?   ☐

4 A teacher tells off 3 children every minute.
   How many children will she tell off in 7 minutes? ☐

5 A horse can run 10 miles in one hour.
   How many miles will the horse run in 3 hours?   ☐ miles

The pirate needs some help to find his treasure. Do the calculation for each path and write the answer in the box.

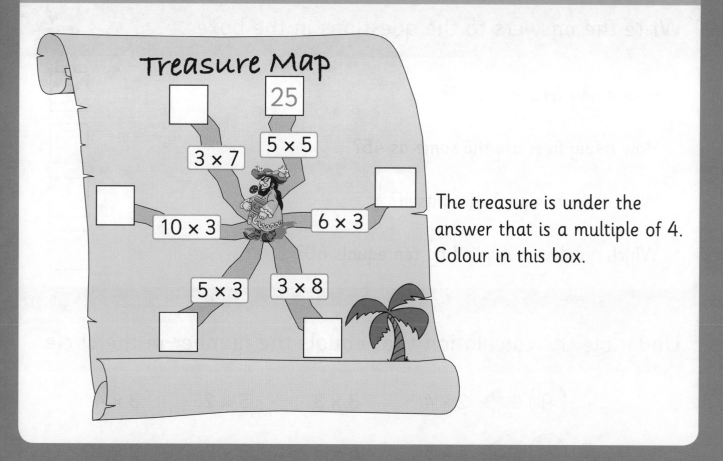

Treasure Map

25

5 × 5

3 × 7

10 × 3

6 × 3

5 × 3

3 × 8

The treasure is under the answer that is a multiple of 4. Colour in this box.

The calculator multiplies each number that goes in by two and then by five. Fill in the missing numbers.

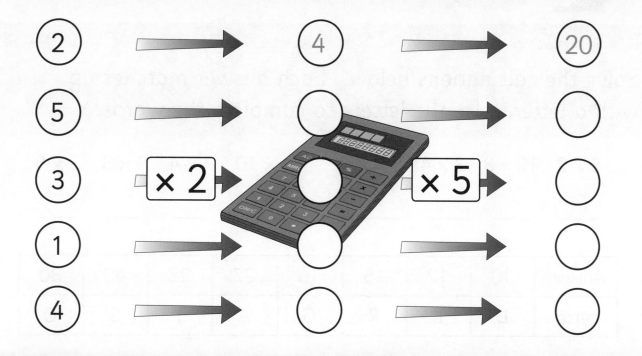

Mixed Questions

Write the answers to the questions in the boxes.

How many tens make 20? `2`

How many fives are the same as 45? `☐`

What is four multiplied by itself? `☐`

Which number multiplied by ten equals 60? `☐`

Underline the calculation that equals the number in the circle.

⑨ ⇒	2 × 4	<u>3 × 3</u>	5 × 2	3 × 4
㉑ ⇒	4 × 5	6 × 3	3 × 7	2 × 10
㉚ ⇒	4 × 7	10 × 3	5 × 7	8 × 4
㊺ ⇒	3 × 8	4 × 5	10 × 4	5 × 9

Solve the calculations below. Each answer matches up with a letter. Use the letters to complete the words.

8 × 2   10 × 8   3 × 4   5 × 2   4 × 10   7 × 4   9 × 3   3 × 5

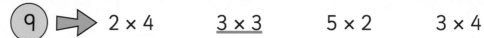
G __ __ __   __ __ __ __

Answer	10	12	15	16	27	28	40	80
Letter	D	L	R	G	A	T	S	O

Write the answers to the questions below.
See how fast you can do them all.

7	×	2	=	14		7	×	☐	=	70
8	×	☐	=	32		☐	×	5	=	5
3	×	9	=	☐		3	×	☐	=	18
☐	×	10	=	10		10	×	4	=	☐
5	×	2	=	☐		4	×	☐	=	36
☐	×	6	=	30		5	×	8	=	☐
4	×	4	=	☐		9	×	☐	=	45
8	×	3	=	☐		10	×	6	=	☐
☐	×	9	=	90		☐	×	7	=	28
5	×	5	=	☐		☐	×	3	=	9
4	×	☐	=	28		3	×	8	=	☐
7	×	☐	=	35		☐	×	4	=	40
☐	×	4	=	12		2	×	☐	=	18
5	×	☐	=	20		5	×	3	=	☐
8	×	2	=	☐		8	×	☐	=	80
4	×	☐	=	24		5	×	7	=	☐
☐	×	3	=	21		☐	×	6	=	30
10	×	10	=	☐		5	×	☐	=	10

SIX times table

Here is the six times table: ➡

Practise the six times table until you can say it from memory. Then write it down without looking.

1	×	6	=	6	
2	×	6	=	12	
3	×	6	=	18	
4	×	6	=	24	
5	×	6	=	30	
6	×	6	=	36	
7	×	6	=	42	
8	×	6	=	48	
9	×	6	=	54	
10	×	6	=	60	

Cover up the six times table above.
Then fill in the blanks in the calculations below.

1	×	6	=	6	
2	×	6	=	☐	
☐	×	6	=	18	
4	×	6	=	☐	
☐	×	6	=	30	

6	×	6	=	☐
☐	×	6	=	42
8	×	6	=	☐
☐	×	6	=	54
10	×	6	=	☐

16

Write the answers to the questions in the boxes.

What is six multiplied by two? | 12 |

How many sixes make 48? | |

What are three sixes? | |

What is six multiplied by four? | |

What is six multiplied by itself? | |

How many sixes are the same as 60? | |

What are nine sixes? | |

These eggs come in boxes of six.
How many eggs are there in each group of boxes?

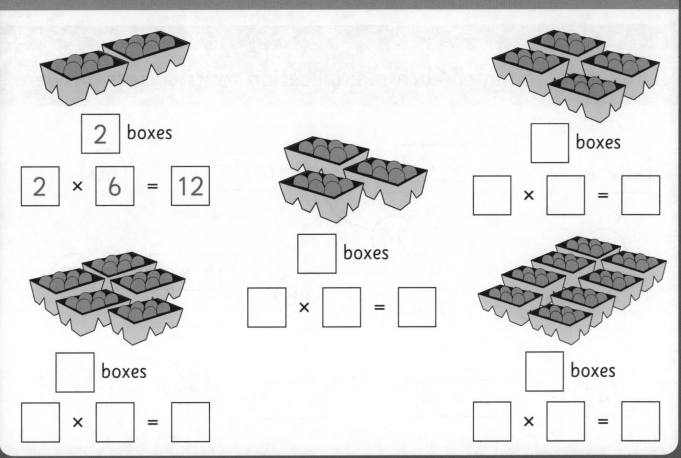

2 boxes

2 × 6 = 12

boxes

□ × □ = □

boxes

□ × □ = □

boxes

□ × □ = □

boxes

□ × □ = □

17

SIX times table

Draw a line from the start of the maze to the finish.
You can only pass through the numbers in the six times table.

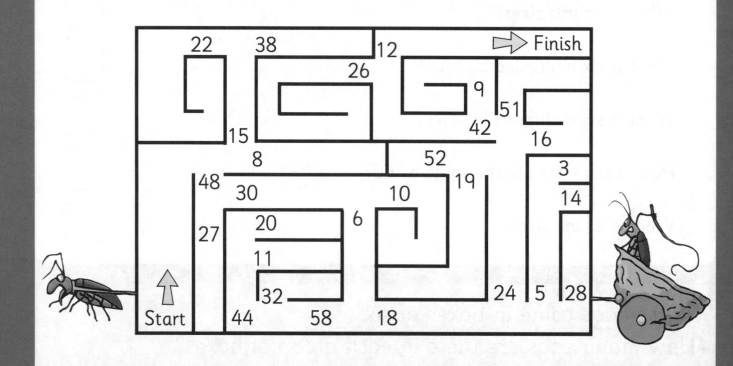

Draw lines to match each multiplication to its correct answer.

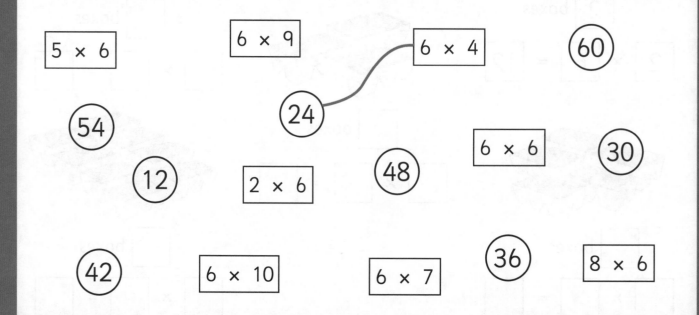

5 × 6

6 × 9

6 × 4

60

54

24

12

2 × 6

48

6 × 6

30

42

6 × 10

6 × 7

36

8 × 6

Write the answers to the questions below.
See how fast you can do them all.

6	×	3	=	18		8	×	6	=	☐
☐	×	6	=	54		5	×	☐	=	30
6	×	☐	=	24		3	×	6	=	☐
2	×	6	=	☐		6	×	☐	=	54
☐	×	6	=	30		☐	×	8	=	48
6	×	☐	=	12		6	×	☐	=	36
9	×	6	=	☐		10	×	6	=	☐
6	×	☐	=	42		☐	×	9	=	54
6	×	8	=	☐		☐	×	6	=	30
6	×	3	=	☐		6	×	7	=	☐
☐	×	10	=	60		☐	×	6	=	18
8	×	☐	=	48		4	×	6	=	☐
6	×	1	=	☐		7	×	☐	=	42
☐	×	6	=	54		6	×	6	=	☐
5	×	6	=	☐		6	×	☐	=	48
☐	×	1	=	6		9	×	☐	=	54
☐	×	6	=	42		6	×	4	=	☐
☐	×	6	=	24		☐	×	6	=	6

SEVEN times table

Here is the seven times table: →

1	×	7	=	7
2	×	7	=	14
3	×	7	=	21
4	×	7	=	28
5	×	7	=	35
6	×	7	=	42
7	×	7	=	49
8	×	7	=	56
9	×	7	=	63
10	×	7	=	70

Write down the seven times table without looking. Then ask a friend to check it for you.

Cover up the seven times table above.
Then fill in the blanks in the calculations below.

1	×	7	=	7		☐	×	7	=	42
☐	×	7	=	14		☐	×	7	=	49
3	×	7	=	☐		8	×	7	=	☐
4	×	7	=	☐		☐	×	7	=	63
☐	×	7	=	35		10	×	7	=	☐

Write the answers to the questions in the boxes.

What are seven threes? `21`

What is seven multiplied by six? ☐

How many sevens make 28? ☐

How many sevens are the same as 63? ☐

What is seven multiplied by seven? ☐

What are eight sevens? ☐

How many sevens are the same as 70? ☐

Fill in the empty circles to complete this number wheel.

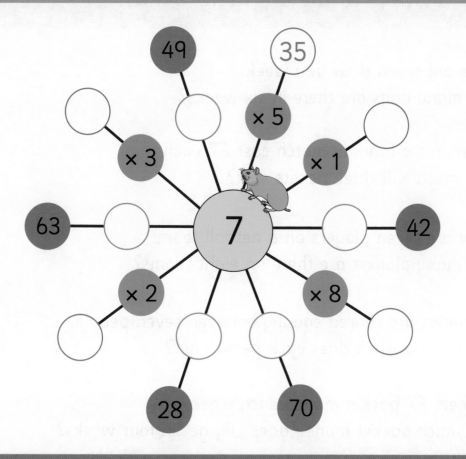

SEVEN times table

One CD costs £7. How much will these sets of CDs cost?

2 CDs

| 2 | × | 7 | = £ | |

3 CDs

| | × | | = £ | |

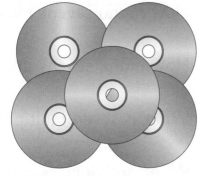

5 CDs

| | × | | = £ | |

Write the answers to the questions below.

1 There are seven days in a week.
How many days are there in six weeks?

2 Tickets for a football match cost £7 each.
How much will three tickets cost?
£

3 There are seven players on a netball team.
How many players are there on eight teams?

4 63 sweets are shared equally between seven people.
How many sweets does each person get?

5 Lily gets £7 pocket money each week.
How much pocket money does Lily get in four weeks?
£

Practise and Learn

Times Tables

Ages 7-11

Answers

Answers

This section shows each of the pages from the book with the answers filled out.

The pages are laid out in the same way as the book itself, so the questions can be easily marked by you, or by your child.

There are also helpful learning tips with some of the pages.

Extension Activities

This book is a great place to start when helping your child to practise their times tables. But there are lots of ways you can add to this using real world examples. For example:

* Tell your child how far they have to travel to get to school each day. Then ask them how far they travel each week.

* Ask your child to count up the number of pairs of socks they own. Then ask them how many socks there are in total.

* In a supermarket, give your child problems to solve using the items you are buying. For example, if a bag of apples contains 6 apples, and you buy 3 bags, ask them how many apples you have bought.

* Ask your child to quiz you on your times tables. Make some deliberate errors and ask them to tell you why you are wrong.

* Give your child a number (e.g. 30). Then ask them to think up any times tables that give that number (e.g. 6 × 5 and 10 × 3).

THREE times table

Here is the three times table: ⟹

Practise the three times table by reading it, covering up the answers, then writing it out.

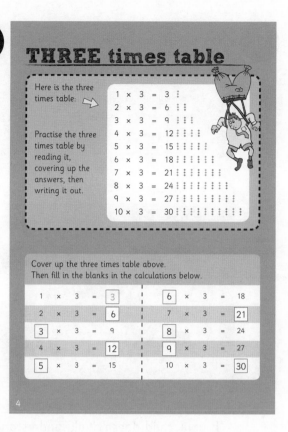

1	×	3	=	3
2	×	3	=	6
3	×	3	=	9
4	×	3	=	12
5	×	3	=	15
6	×	3	=	18
7	×	3	=	21
8	×	3	=	24
9	×	3	=	27
10	×	3	=	30

Cover up the three times table above.
Then fill in the blanks in the calculations below.

1	×	3	=	3		6	×	3	=	18
2	×	3	=	6		7	×	3	=	21
3	×	3	=	9		8	×	3	=	24
4	×	3	=	12		9	×	3	=	27
5	×	3	=	15		10	×	3	=	30

Write the answers to the questions in the boxes.

What are six threes?	18
What is three multiplied by eight?	24
How many threes make 30?	10
How many threes are the same as 21?	7
What is three multiplied by five?	15
How many threes are the same as 12?	4
What are nine threes?	27

How many footballs are there in each set in total?

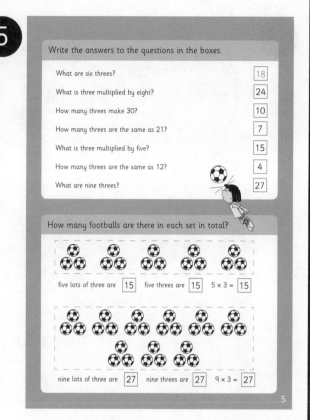

five lots of three are 15   five threes are 15   5 × 3 = 15

nine lots of three are 27   nine threes are 27   9 × 3 = 27

THREE times table

Write the answers to the questions in the boxes.

1. A box of nails contains 10 nails. A man buys three boxes. How many nails does he buy?   30

2. Draw a line to make a path from the start to the finish. You can only go through the numbers in the three times table.

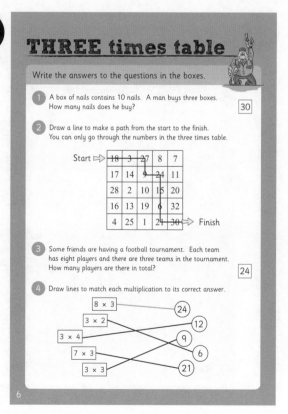

Start ⟹

18	3	27	8	7
17	14	9	24	11
28	2	10	15	20
16	13	19	6	32
4	25	1	21	30

⟹ Finish

3. Some friends are having a football tournament. Each team has eight players and there are three teams in the tournament. How many players are there in total?   24

4. Draw lines to match each multiplication to its correct answer.

8 × 3 — 24
3 × 2 — 12
3 × 4 — 9
7 × 3 — 6
3 × 3 — 21

Write the answers to the questions below.
See how fast you can do them all.

5	×	3	=	15		3	×	9	=	27
1	×	3	=	3		3	×	7	=	21
7	×	3	=	21		8	×	3	=	24
3	×	3	=	9		3	×	7	=	21
6	×	3	=	18		3	×	8	=	24
9	×	3	=	27		9	×	3	=	27
3	×	2	=	6		3	×	3	=	9
3	×	5	=	15		7	×	3	=	21
6	×	3	=	18		3	×	4	=	12
8	×	3	=	24		3	×	1	=	3
3	×	4	=	12		3	×	8	=	24
3	×	9	=	27		10	×	3	=	30
3	×	8	=	24		4	×	3	=	12
3	×	7	=	21		3	×	9	=	27
2	×	3	=	6		7	×	3	=	21
3	×	6	=	18		8	×	3	=	24
9	×	3	=	27		4	×	3	=	12
3	×	10	=	30		3	×	6	=	18

If your child enjoys seeing how fast they can do these pages, keep a note of their time for each times table so they can see which ones they're fastest at.

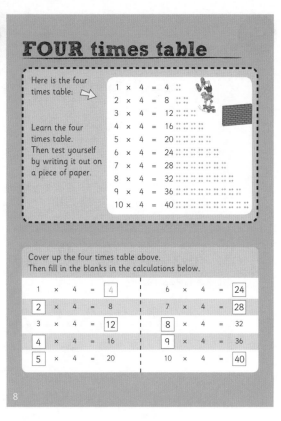

8

FOUR times table

Here is the four
times table: →

$1 \times 4 = 4$
$2 \times 4 = 8$
$3 \times 4 = 12$
$4 \times 4 = 16$
$5 \times 4 = 20$
$6 \times 4 = 24$
$7 \times 4 = 28$
$8 \times 4 = 32$
$9 \times 4 = 36$
$10 \times 4 = 40$

Learn the four
times table.
Then test yourself
by writing it out on
a piece of paper.

Cover up the four times table above.
Then fill in the blanks in the calculations below.

1	×	4	=	4		6	×	4	=	24
2	×	4	=	8		7	×	4	=	28
3	×	4	=	12		8	×	4	=	32
4	×	4	=	16		9	×	4	=	36
5	×	4	=	20		10	×	4	=	40

8

9

Write the answers to the questions in the boxes.

What is four multiplied by two? — 8

What are eight fours? — 32

How many fours are the same as 16? — 4

How many fours make 40? — 10

What is four multiplied by five? — 20

How many fours are the same as 28? — 7

What are three fours? — 12

How many legs are there in each set of cats and dogs?

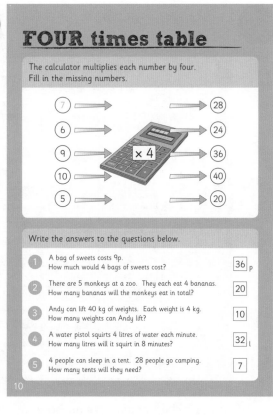

2 dogs
$2 \times 4 = 8$

3 cats
$3 \times 4 = 12$

4 cats
$4 \times 4 = 16$

5 dogs
$5 \times 4 = 20$

6 dogs
$6 \times 4 = 24$

9

If your child doesn't fully understand
the question, try talking them through
the example to show them how to fill
in the boxes.

10

FOUR times table

The calculator multiplies each number by four.
Fill in the missing numbers.

$7 \rightarrow \boxed{\times 4} \rightarrow 28$
$6 \rightarrow 24$
$9 \rightarrow 36$
$10 \rightarrow 40$
$5 \rightarrow 20$

Write the answers to the questions below.

1. A bag of sweets costs 9p.
   How much would 4 bags of sweets cost? — 36 p

2. There are 5 monkeys at a zoo. They each eat 4 bananas.
   How many bananas will the monkeys eat in total? — 20

3. Andy can lift 40 kg of weights. Each weight is 4 kg.
   How many weights can Andy lift? — 10

4. A water pistol squirts 4 litres of water each minute.
   How many litres will it squirt in 8 minutes? — 32 l

5. 4 people can sleep in a tent. 28 people go camping.
   How many tents will they need? — 7

10

11

Write the answers to the questions below.
See how fast you can do them all.

8	×	4	=	32		4	×	3	=	12
7	×	4	=	28		4	×	8	=	32
4	×	9	=	36		6	×	4	=	24
4	×	1	=	4		5	×	4	=	20
2	×	4	=	8		9	×	4	=	36
5	×	4	=	20		4	×	7	=	28
4	×	6	=	24		4	×	4	=	16
4	×	3	=	12		8	×	4	=	32
4	×	7	=	28		4	×	5	=	20
4	×	9	=	36		4	×	10	=	40
1	×	4	=	4		9	×	4	=	36
4	×	6	=	24		8	×	4	=	32
10	×	4	=	40		4	×	4	=	16
4	×	2	=	8		7	×	4	=	28
5	×	4	=	20		3	×	4	=	12
9	×	4	=	36		4	×	5	=	20
4	×	8	=	32		4	×	8	=	32
7	×	4	=	28		6	×	4	=	24

11

Mixed Questions

Fill in the boxes to show how much it would cost to buy these items.

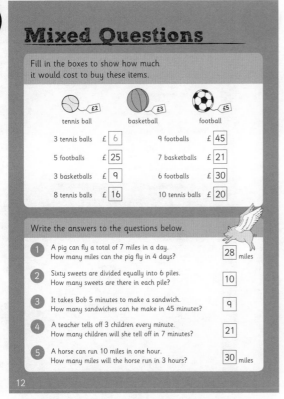

tennis ball — £2
basketball — £3
football — £5

3 tennis balls £ 6
5 footballs £ 25
3 basketballs £ 9
8 tennis balls £ 16

9 footballs £ 45
7 basketballs £ 21
6 footballs £ 30
10 tennis balls £ 20

Write the answers to the questions below.

1 A pig can fly a total of 7 miles in a day. How many miles can the pig fly in 4 days? 28 miles

2 Sixty sweets are divided equally into 6 piles. How many sweets are there in each pile? 10

3 It takes Bob 5 minutes to make a sandwich. How many sandwiches can he make in 45 minutes? 9

4 A teacher tells off 3 children every minute. How many children will she tell off in 7 minutes? 21

5 A horse can run 10 miles in one hour. How many miles will the horse run in 3 hours? 30 miles

If your child is confused by these pages, make sure they understand that the questions are on a mixture of the times tables.

The pirate needs some help to find his treasure. Do the calculation for each path and write the answer in the box.

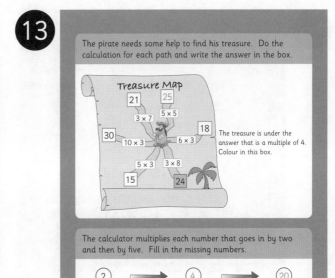

Treasure Map

21
25
3 × 7
5 × 5
30
10 × 3
6 × 3
18
5 × 3
3 × 8
15
24

The treasure is under the answer that is a multiple of 4. Colour in this box.

The calculator multiplies each number that goes in by two and then by five. Fill in the missing numbers.

2 → ×2 → 4 → ×5 → 20
5 → → 10 → → 50
3 → → 6 → → 30
1 → → 2 → → 10
4 → → 8 → → 40

Mixed Questions

Write the answers to the questions in the boxes.

How many tens make 20? 2
How many fives are the same as 45? 9
What is four multiplied by itself? 16
Which number multiplied by ten equals 60? 6

Underline the calculation that equals the number in the circle.

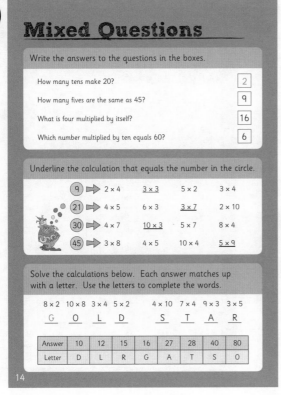

9 ➡ 2 × 4   3 × 3   5 × 2   3 × 4
21 ➡ 4 × 5   6 × 3   3 × 7   2 × 10
30 ➡ 4 × 7   10 × 3   5 × 7   8 × 4
45 ➡ 3 × 8   4 × 5   10 × 4   5 × 9

Solve the calculations below. Each answer matches up with a letter. Use the letters to complete the words.

8 × 2 10 × 8 3 × 4 5 × 2   4 × 10 7 × 4 9 × 3 3 × 5
G   O   L   D   S   T   A   R

Answer	10	12	15	16	27	28	40	80
Letter	D	L	R	G	A	T	S	O

Write the answers to the questions below. See how fast you can do them all.

7	×	2	=	14	7	×	10	=	70
8	×	4	=	32	1	×	5	=	5
3	×	9	=	27	3	×	6	=	18
1	×	10	=	10	10	×	4	=	40
5	×	2	=	10	4	×	9	=	36
5	×	6	=	30	5	×	8	=	40
4	×	4	=	16	9	×	5	=	45
8	×	3	=	24	10	×	6	=	60
10	×	9	=	90	4	×	7	=	28
5	×	5	=	25	3	×	3	=	9
4	×	7	=	28	3	×	8	=	24
7	×	5	=	35	10	×	4	=	40
3	×	4	=	12	2	×	9	=	18
5	×	4	=	20	5	×	3	=	15
8	×	2	=	16	8	×	10	=	80
4	×	6	=	24	5	×	7	=	35
7	×	3	=	21	5	×	6	=	30
10	×	10	=	100	5	×	2	=	10

SIX times table

Here is the six times table: ➡

Practise the six times table until you can say it from memory. Then write it down without looking.

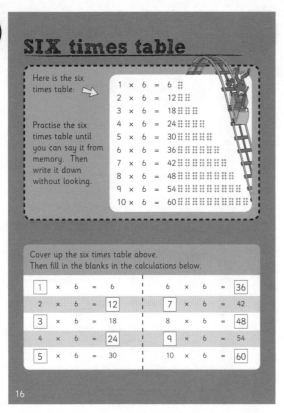

```
1  × 6 = 6
2  × 6 = 12
3  × 6 = 18
4  × 6 = 24
5  × 6 = 30
6  × 6 = 36
7  × 6 = 42
8  × 6 = 48
9  × 6 = 54
10 × 6 = 60
```

Cover up the six times table above.
Then fill in the blanks in the calculations below.

1	×	6	=	6		6	×	6	=	36
2	×	6	=	12		7	×	6	=	42
3	×	6	=	18		8	×	6	=	48
4	×	6	=	24		9	×	6	=	54
5	×	6	=	30		10	×	6	=	60

Write the answers to the questions in the boxes.

What is six multiplied by two? **12**

How many sixes make 48? **8**

What are three sixes? **18**

What is six multiplied by four? **24**

What is six multiplied by itself? **36**

How many sixes are the same as 60? **10**

What are nine sixes? **54**

These eggs come in boxes of six.
How many eggs are there in each group of boxes?

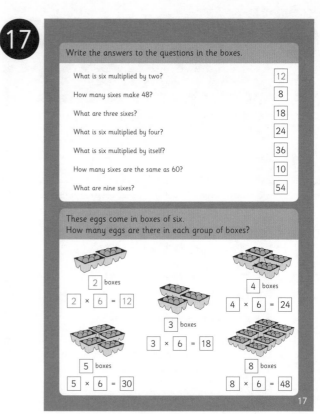

2 boxes
$2 × 6 = 12$

4 boxes
$4 × 6 = 24$

3 boxes
$3 × 6 = 18$

5 boxes
$5 × 6 = 30$

8 boxes
$8 × 6 = 48$

SIX times table

Draw a line from the start of the maze to the finish.
You can only pass through the numbers in the six times table.

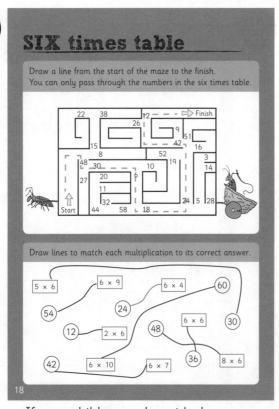

Draw lines to match each multiplication to its correct answer.

5 × 6   6 × 9   6 × 4   60
54   24
12   2 × 6   48   30
6 × 6
42   6 × 10   6 × 7   36   8 × 6

If your child struggles with the maze question, ask them to write out their six times table on a separate piece of paper and try again.

Write the answers to the questions below.
See how fast you can do them all.

6	×	3	=	18		8	×	6	=	48
9	×	6	=	54		5	×	6	=	30
6	×	4	=	24		3	×	6	=	18
2	×	6	=	12		6	×	9	=	54
5	×	6	=	30		6	×	8	=	48
6	×	2	=	12		6	×	6	=	36
9	×	6	=	54		10	×	6	=	60
6	×	7	=	42		6	×	9	=	54
6	×	8	=	48		5	×	6	=	30
6	×	3	=	18		6	×	7	=	42
6	×	10	=	60		3	×	6	=	18
8	×	6	=	48		4	×	6	=	24
6	×	1	=	6		7	×	6	=	42
9	×	6	=	54		6	×	6	=	36
5	×	6	=	30		6	×	8	=	48
6	×	1	=	6		9	×	6	=	54
7	×	6	=	42		6	×	4	=	24
4	×	6	=	24		1	×	6	=	6

SEVEN times table

Here is the seven times table:

Write down the seven times table without looking. Then ask a friend to check it for you.

1	×	7	=	7
2	×	7	=	14
3	×	7	=	21
4	×	7	=	28
5	×	7	=	35
6	×	7	=	42
7	×	7	=	49
8	×	7	=	56
9	×	7	=	63
10	×	7	=	70

Cover up the seven times table above.
Then fill in the blanks in the calculations below.

1	×	7	=	7		6	×	7	=	42
2	×	7	=	14		7	×	7	=	49
3	×	7	=	21		8	×	7	=	56
4	×	7	=	28		9	×	7	=	63
5	×	7	=	35		10	×	7	=	70

Write the answers to the questions in the boxes.

What are seven threes?	21
What is seven multiplied by six?	42
How many sevens make 28?	4
How many sevens are the same as 63?	9
What is seven multiplied by seven?	49
What are eight sevens?	56
How many sevens are the same as 70?	10

Fill in the empty circles to complete this number wheel.

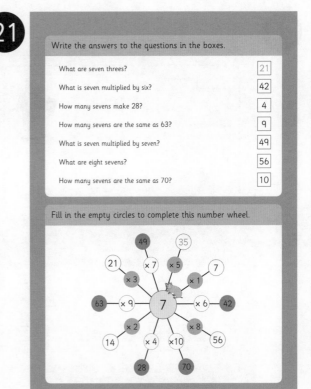

SEVEN times table

One CD costs £7. How much will these sets of CDs cost?

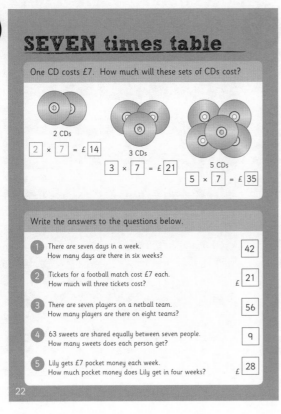

2 CDs
2 × 7 = £ 14

3 CDs
3 × 7 = £ 21

5 CDs
5 × 7 = £ 35

Write the answers to the questions below.

1. There are seven days in a week.
How many days are there in six weeks? — 42

2. Tickets for a football match cost £7 each.
How much will three tickets cost? — £ 21

3. There are seven players on a netball team.
How many players are there on eight teams? — 56

4. 63 sweets are shared equally between seven people.
How many sweets does each person get? — 9

5. Lily gets £7 pocket money each week.
How much pocket money does Lily get in four weeks? — £ 28

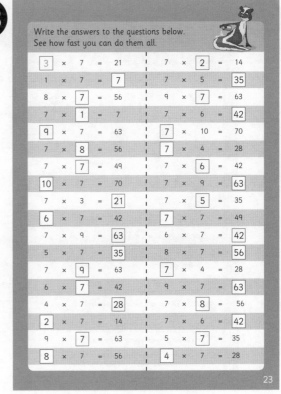

Write the answers to the questions below.
See how fast you can do them all.

3	×	7	=	21		7	×	2	=	14
1	×	7	=	7		7	×	5	=	35
8	×	7	=	56		9	×	7	=	63
7	×	1	=	7		7	×	6	=	42
9	×	7	=	63		7	×	10	=	70
7	×	8	=	56		7	×	4	=	28
7	×	7	=	49		7	×	6	=	42
10	×	7	=	70		7	×	9	=	63
7	×	3	=	21		7	×	5	=	35
6	×	7	=	42		7	×	7	=	49
7	×	9	=	63		6	×	7	=	42
5	×	7	=	35		8	×	7	=	56
7	×	9	=	63		7	×	4	=	28
6	×	7	=	42		9	×	7	=	63
4	×	7	=	28		7	×	8	=	56
2	×	7	=	14		7	×	6	=	42
9	×	7	=	63		5	×	7	=	35
8	×	7	=	56		4	×	7	=	28

If your child is having difficulty with some of these questions try explaining that it doesn't matter if the numbers have been switched round. So 3 × 7 is the same as 7 × 3.

EIGHT times table

Here is the eight times table: ➡

1	×	8	=	8
2	×	8	=	16
3	×	8	=	24
4	×	8	=	32
5	×	8	=	40
6	×	8	=	48
7	×	8	=	56
8	×	8	=	64
9	×	8	=	72
10	×	8	=	80

Remember — all of the numbers in the eight times table are even numbers.

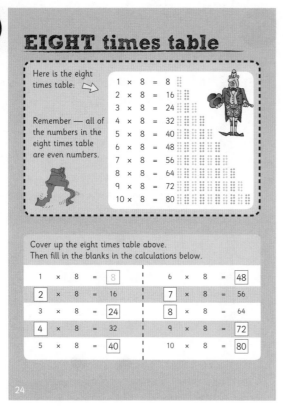

Cover up the eight times table above.
Then fill in the blanks in the calculations below.

1	×	8	=	8		6	×	8	=	48
2	×	8	=	16		7	×	8	=	56
3	×	8	=	24		8	×	8	=	64
4	×	8	=	32		9	×	8	=	72
5	×	8	=	40		10	×	8	=	80

Write the answers to the questions in the boxes.

What is eight multiplied by two?	16
What is eight multiplied by itself?	64
What are eight nines?	72
What is eight multiplied by ten?	80
How many eights make 40?	5
What is four multiplied by eight?	32
How many eights are the same as 56?	7

Colour in the multiples of eight in the table below.

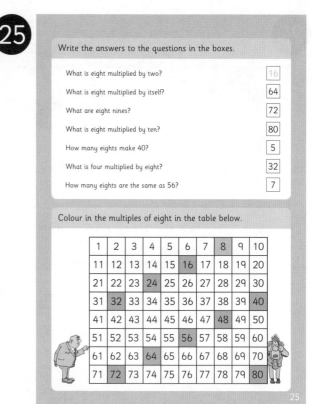

1	2	3	4	5	6	7	8	9	10
11	12	13	14	15	16	17	18	19	20
21	22	23	24	25	26	27	28	29	30
31	32	33	34	35	36	37	38	39	40
41	42	43	44	45	46	47	48	49	50
51	52	53	54	55	56	57	58	59	60
61	62	63	64	65	66	67	68	69	70
71	72	73	74	75	76	77	78	79	80

EIGHT times table

An octopus has 8 arms.
How many arms are there in each set?

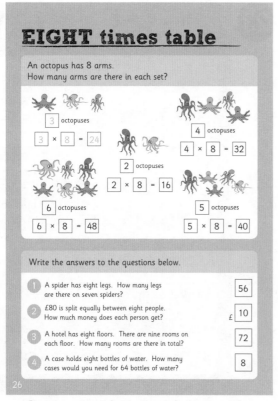

3 octopuses
3 × 8 = 24

4 octopuses
4 × 8 = 32

2 octopuses
2 × 8 = 16

6 octopuses
6 × 8 = 48

5 octopuses
5 × 8 = 40

Write the answers to the questions below.

1. A spider has eight legs. How many legs are there on seven spiders? — 56
2. £80 is split equally between eight people. How much money does each person get? — £10
3. A hotel has eight floors. There are nine rooms on each floor. How many rooms are there in total? — 72
4. A case holds eight bottles of water. How many cases would you need for 64 bottles of water? — 8

Write the answers to the questions below.
See how fast you can do them all.

3	×	8	=	24		8	×	10	=	80
4	×	8	=	32		8	×	9	=	72
8	×	7	=	56		8	×	4	=	32
8	×	1	=	8		8	×	6	=	48
9	×	8	=	72		5	×	8	=	40
8	×	4	=	32		8	×	9	=	72
2	×	8	=	16		8	×	8	=	64
8	×	3	=	24		8	×	3	=	24
8	×	10	=	80		7	×	8	=	56
6	×	8	=	48		8	×	6	=	48
8	×	5	=	40		10	×	8	=	80
8	×	8	=	64		8	×	2	=	16
9	×	8	=	72		5	×	8	=	40
8	×	7	=	56		1	×	8	=	8
4	×	8	=	32		9	×	8	=	72
8	×	5	=	40		5	×	8	=	40
6	×	8	=	48		7	×	8	=	56
8	×	9	=	72		8	×	8	=	64

1+1=2

Questions without visual cues can be a real challenge for some children. Some objects to count (e.g. buttons or counters) can be really helpful.

NINE times table

Here is the nine times table: ➡

The numbers in each answer to the nine times table add up to nine.

For example:
18
1 + 8 = 9

1	×	9	=	9
2	×	9	=	18
3	×	9	=	27
4	×	9	=	36
5	×	9	=	45
6	×	9	=	54
7	×	9	=	63
8	×	9	=	72
9	×	9	=	81
10	×	9	=	90

Cover up the nine times table above.
Then fill in the blanks in the calculations below.

1	×	9	=	9	**6**	×	9	=	**54**
2	×	9	=	18	7	×	9	=	**63**
3	×	9	=	27	**8**	×	9	=	72
4	×	9	=	**36**	**9**	×	9	=	81
5	×	9	=	**45**	10	×	9	=	**90**

28

Write the answers to the questions in the boxes.

How many nines make 18?	2
What is nine multiplied by seven?	63
What are five nines?	45
How many nines are the same as 81?	9
What is six multiplied by nine?	54
What is ten multiplied by nine?	90
How many eights make 72?	9

Five friends go shopping for some new T-shirts.
Work out how much they each spend.

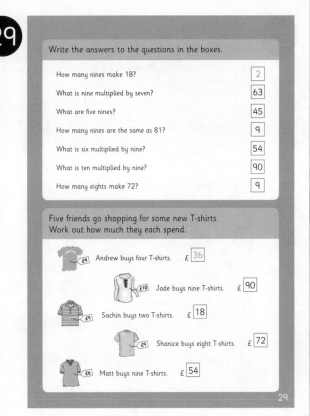

£9 — Andrew buys four T-shirts. £ 36

£10 — Jade buys nine T-shirts. £ 90

£9 — Sachin buys two T-shirts. £ 18

£9 — Shanice buys eight T-shirts. £ 72

£6 — Matt buys nine T-shirts. £ 54

29

NINE times table

Solve the calculations below. Each answer matches up with a letter. Use the letters to complete the words.

4×9 9×8 9×2 3×9 7×9   9×9 9×10 8×9 9×6
 G   R   E   A   T   W   O   R   K

Answer	18	27	36	54	63	72	81	90
Letter	E	A	G	K	T	R	W	O

Colour in each part of the picture that has a multiple of nine.

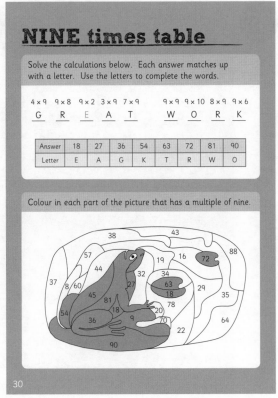

30

Write the answers to the questions below.
See how fast you can do them all.

9	×	1	=	9		10	×	9	=	**90**
8	×	9	=	72		9	×	**7**	=	63
9	×	5	=	**45**		9	×	3	=	**27**
6	×	9	=	54		9	×	**9**	=	81
9	×	7	=	63		**9**	×	8	=	72
9	×	2	=	**18**		7	×	**9**	=	63
8	×	**9**	=	72		4	×	**9**	=	36
6	×	9	=	**54**		9	×	9	=	**81**
7	×	9	=	**63**		5	×	9	=	**45**
9	×	9	=	**81**		**6**	×	9	=	54
3	×	9	=	27		3	×	9	=	**27**
9	×	**8**	=	72		9	×	**1**	=	9
9	×	**4**	=	36		**7**	×	9	=	63
9	×	7	=	**63**		8	×	9	=	**72**
9	×	6	=	54		9	×	**4**	=	36
4	×	9	=	**36**		**9**	×	10	=	90
9	×	**2**	=	18		9	×	**8**	=	72
7	×	9	=	63		9	×	9	=	**81**

31

Cracking the code questions can be a lot of fun. If your child enjoys them, try asking them to write some codes for you to crack.

32 — ELEVEN times table

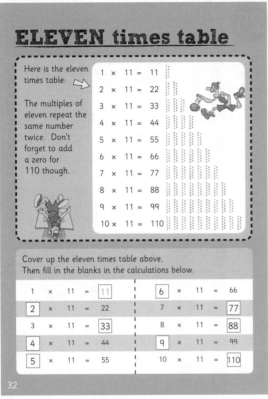

Here is the eleven times table: ➡

The multiples of eleven repeat the same number twice. Don't forget to add a zero for 110 though.

1	×	11	=	11
2	×	11	=	22
3	×	11	=	33
4	×	11	=	44
5	×	11	=	55
6	×	11	=	66
7	×	11	=	77
8	×	11	=	88
9	×	11	=	99
10	×	11	=	110

Cover up the eleven times table above.
Then fill in the blanks in the calculations below.

1	×	11	=	11		6	×	11	=	66
2	×	11	=	22		7	×	11	=	77
3	×	11	=	33		8	×	11	=	88
4	×	11	=	44		9	×	11	=	99
5	×	11	=	55		10	×	11	=	110

32

33

Write the answers to the questions in the boxes.

How many elevens are the same as 44?	4
What are seven elevens?	77
What is two multiplied by eleven?	22
What is ten multiplied by eleven?	110
How many elevens make 33?	3
How many elevens are the same as 99?	9
How many elevens make 88?	8
What is five multiplied by eleven?	55

The calculator multiplies each number by eleven.
Fill in the missing numbers.

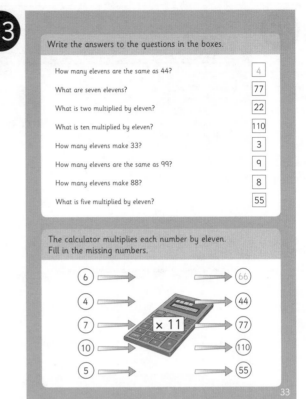

6 → → 66
4 → → 44
7 → × 11 → 77
10 → → 110
5 → → 55

33

Make sure your child understands that the number being multiplied by eleven will make up two digits of the answer. This should help them to answer questions on the eleven times table.

34 — ELEVEN times table

A car is on a roundabout. It only drives on roads that are multiples of eleven. How many roads can the car drive on?

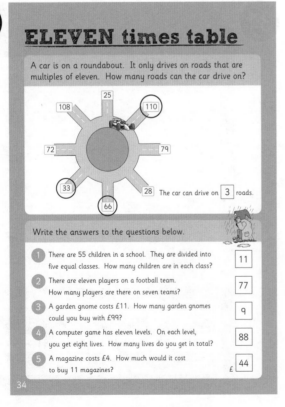

25
108   110
72   79
33
28   The car can drive on 3 roads.
66

Write the answers to the questions below.

1. There are 55 children in a school. They are divided into five equal classes. How many children are in each class? — 11

2. There are eleven players on a football team. How many players are there on seven teams? — 77

3. A garden gnome costs £11. How many garden gnomes could you buy with £99? — 9

4. A computer game has eleven levels. On each level, you get eight lives. How many lives do you get in total? — 88

5. A magazine costs £4. How much would it cost to buy 11 magazines? — £ 44

34

35

Write the answers to the questions below.
See how fast you can do them all.

3	×	11	=	33		11	×	8	=	88
7	×	11	=	77		11	×	9	=	99
4	×	11	=	44		7	×	11	=	77
11	×	1	=	11		4	×	11	=	44
11	×	6	=	66		11	×	3	=	33
11	×	4	=	44		9	×	11	=	99
8	×	11	=	88		1	×	11	=	11
11	×	7	=	77		11	×	10	=	110
9	×	11	=	99		8	×	11	=	88
10	×	11	=	110		11	×	6	=	66
2	×	11	=	22		11	×	7	=	77
11	×	9	=	99		11	×	8	=	88
5	×	11	=	55		11	×	4	=	44
6	×	11	=	66		1	×	11	=	11
9	×	11	=	99		10	×	11	=	110
7	×	11	=	77		11	×	5	=	55
8	×	11	=	88		9	×	11	=	99
11	×	2	=	22		6	×	11	=	66

35

TWELVE times table

Here is the twelve times table: ➡

The answers to the twelve times table are double the answers to the six times table.

For example:
$2 \times 6 = 12$
$2 \times 12 = 24$

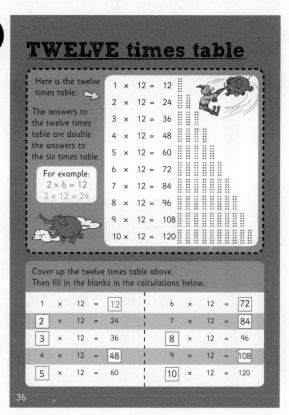

1	×	12	=	12	
2	×	12	=	24	
3	×	12	=	36	
4	×	12	=	48	
5	×	12	=	60	
6	×	12	=	72	
7	×	12	=	84	
8	×	12	=	96	
9	×	12	=	108	
10	×	12	=	120	

Cover up the twelve times table above.
Then fill in the blanks in the calculations below.

1	×	12	=	12		6	×	12	=	72
2	×	12	=	24		7	×	12	=	84
3	×	12	=	36		8	×	12	=	96
4	×	12	=	48		9	×	12	=	108
5	×	12	=	60		10	×	12	=	120

Write the answers to the questions in the boxes.

What are four twelves? — 48

How many twelves are the same as 96? — 8

What is seven multiplied by twelve? — 84

What is three multiplied by twelve? — 36

How many twelves make 60? — 5

How many twelves are the same as 108? — 9

Doughnuts come in boxes of twelve.
How many doughnuts are in each set? = 12 doughnuts

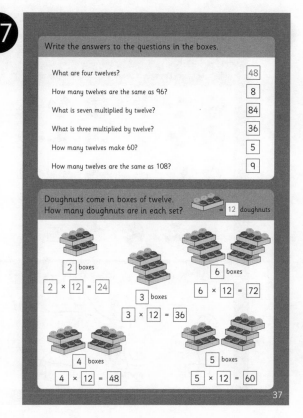

2 boxes
$2 \times 12 = 24$

6 boxes
$6 \times 12 = 72$

3 boxes
$3 \times 12 = 36$

4 boxes
$4 \times 12 = 48$

5 boxes
$5 \times 12 = 60$

TWELVE times table

Answer the questions below.

1 Circle the calculation below that would give the answer 84.

10 × 12	12 × 8	12 × 6
(7 × 12)	9 × 12	12 × 4

2 Draw a line to make a path from the start to the finish.
You can only go through the numbers in the twelve times table.

Start ➡
48	24	40	8	77
32	36	98	46	92
108	12	104	62	80
96	88	110	16	34
60	72	84	120	24
➡ Finish

3 A ticket to a theme park costs £12. Answer the questions below.

How many tickets can you buy with £24? — 2

How much will it cost to buy six tickets? — £72

How much will it cost to buy five tickets? — £60

How many tickets can you buy with £108? — 9

How much will it cost to buy ten tickets? — £120

How many tickets can you buy with £84? — 7

Write the answers to the questions below.
See how fast you can do them all.

3	×	12	=	36		8	×	12	=	96
12	×	9	=	108		12	×	4	=	48
12	×	5	=	60		7	×	12	=	84
10	×	12	=	120		12	×	1	=	12
8	×	12	=	96		7	×	12	=	84
12	×	7	=	84		8	×	12	=	96
12	×	2	=	24		9	×	12	=	108
9	×	12	=	108		6	×	12	=	72
10	×	12	=	120		12	×	4	=	48
12	×	4	=	48		12	×	9	=	108
8	×	12	=	96		12	×	7	=	84
6	×	12	=	72		12	×	8	=	96
12	×	1	=	12		3	×	12	=	36
12	×	7	=	84		12	×	6	=	72
1	×	12	=	12		9	×	12	=	108
12	×	9	=	108		7	×	12	=	84
5	×	12	=	60		12	×	2	=	24
12	×	6	=	72		4	×	12	=	48

Mixed Questions

Multiply together the numbers that the arrow is pointing to.

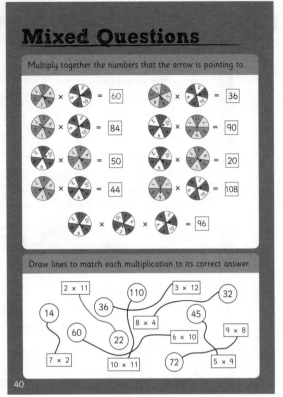

○ × ○ = 60		○ × ○ = 36
○ × ○ = 84		○ × ○ = 90
○ × ○ = 50		○ × ○ = 20
○ × ○ = 44		○ × ○ = 108
○ × ○ × ○ = 96		

Draw lines to match each multiplication to its correct answer.

2 × 11   110   3 × 12   32
14   36   45
60   8 × 4   22
7 × 2   6 × 10   9 × 8
10 × 11   72   5 × 9

40

Write the answers to the questions in the boxes.

What are three sevens?	21
What is nine multiplied by three?	27
What is twelve multiplied by seven?	84
How many threes make 33?	11
How many elevens are the same as 55?	5
What is seven multiplied by itself?	49
What are ten twelves?	120

Fill in the boxes to show how much it would cost to buy the following pets in a pet shop.

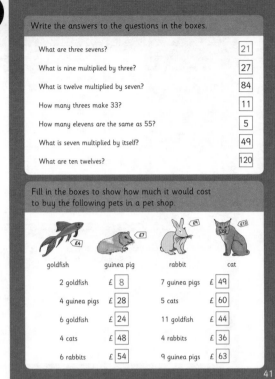

goldfish   guinea pig   rabbit   cat

2 goldfish	£ 8	7 guinea pigs	£ 49
4 guinea pigs	£ 28	5 cats	£ 60
6 goldfish	£ 24	11 goldfish	£ 44
4 cats	£ 48	4 rabbits	£ 36
6 rabbits	£ 54	9 guinea pigs	£ 63

41

Mixed Questions

Complete the multiplication grid.

×	1	2	3	4	5	6	7	8	9	10
1	1	2	3	4	5	6	7	8	9	10
2	2	4	6	8	10	12	14	16	18	20
3	3	6	9	12	15	18	21	24	27	30
4	4	8	12	16	20	24	28	32	36	40
5	5	10	15	20	25	30	35	40	45	50
6	6	12	18	24	30	36	42	48	54	60
7	7	14	21	28	35	42	49	56	63	70
8	8	16	24	32	40	48	56	64	72	80
9	9	18	27	36	45	54	63	72	81	90
10	10	20	30	40	50	60	70	80	90	100
11	11	22	33	44	55	66	77	88	99	110
12	12	24	36	48	60	72	84	96	108	120

Underline the calculation that equals the number in the circle.

36	➡	6 × 7	7 × 5	<u>4 × 9</u>	10 × 4
50	➡	9 × 5	8 × 6	<u>5 × 10</u>	6 × 10
64	➡	12 × 5	<u>8 × 8</u>	10 × 6	7 × 9
96	➡	7 × 12	10 × 9	12 × 9	<u>12 × 8</u>

42

Write the answers to the questions below.
See how fast you can do them all.

7	×	2	=	14	12	×	9	=	108
11	×	7	=	77	10	×	4	=	40
5	×	6	=	30	7	×	12	=	84
10	×	2	=	20	3	×	1	=	3
7	×	3	=	21	9	×	2	=	18
9	×	12	=	108	10	×	12	=	120
3	×	5	=	15	9	×	5	=	45
10	×	7	=	70	6	×	11	=	66
8	×	12	=	96	12	×	4	=	48
5	×	12	=	60	11	×	3	=	33
2	×	6	=	12	9	×	7	=	63
7	×	8	=	56	7	×	6	=	42
6	×	9	=	54	11	×	8	=	88
3	×	11	=	33	8	×	12	=	96
2	×	8	=	16	7	×	4	=	28
9	×	4	=	36	11	×	9	=	99
12	×	3	=	36	6	×	6	=	36
4	×	4	=	16	5	×	4	=	20

43

When your child has filled in the multiplication grid, ask them to read across each row to recite the multiples of each number. This may help them to notice any mistakes that they may have made.

Write the answers to the questions below.
See how fast you can do them all.

3	×	7	=	21		7	×	☐	=	14
1	×	7	=	☐		7	×	5	=	☐
8	×	☐	=	56		9	×	☐	=	63
7	×	☐	=	7		7	×	6	=	☐
☐	×	7	=	63		☐	×	10	=	70
7	×	☐	=	56		☐	×	4	=	28
7	×	☐	=	49		7	×	☐	=	42
☐	×	7	=	70		7	×	9	=	☐
7	×	3	=	☐		7	×	☐	=	35
☐	×	7	=	42		☐	×	7	=	49
7	×	9	=	☐		6	×	7	=	☐
5	×	7	=	☐		8	×	7	=	☐
7	×	☐	=	63		☐	×	4	=	28
6	×	☐	=	42		9	×	7	=	☐
4	×	7	=	☐		7	×	☐	=	56
☐	×	7	=	14		7	×	6	=	☐
9	×	☐	=	63		5	×	☐	=	35
☐	×	7	=	56		☐	×	7	=	28

23

EIGHT times table

Here is the eight times table: ⇨

Remember — all of the numbers in the eight times table are even numbers.

1	×	8	=	8
2	×	8	=	16
3	×	8	=	24
4	×	8	=	32
5	×	8	=	40
6	×	8	=	48
7	×	8	=	56
8	×	8	=	64
9	×	8	=	72
10	×	8	=	80

Cover up the eight times table above.
Then fill in the blanks in the calculations below.

1	×	8	=	8		6	×	8	=	☐
☐	×	8	=	16		☐	×	8	=	56
3	×	8	=	☐		☐	×	8	=	64
☐	×	8	=	32		9	×	8	=	☐
5	×	8	=	☐		10	×	8	=	☐

24

Write the answers to the questions in the boxes.

What is eight multiplied by two? `16`

What is eight multiplied by itself?

What are eight nines?

What is eight multiplied by ten?

How many eights make 40?

What is four multiplied by eight?

How many eights are the same as 56?

Colour in the multiples of eight in the table below.

1	2	3	4	5	6	7	8	9	10
11	12	13	14	15	16	17	18	19	20
21	22	23	24	25	26	27	28	29	30
31	32	33	34	35	36	37	38	39	40
41	42	43	44	45	46	47	48	49	50
51	52	53	54	55	56	57	58	59	60
61	62	63	64	65	66	67	68	69	70
71	72	73	74	75	76	77	78	79	80

25

EIGHT times table

An octopus has 8 arms.
How many arms are there in each set?

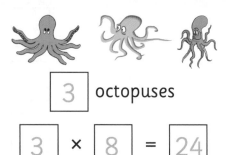

3 octopuses

3 × 8 = 24

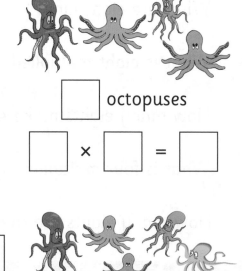

☐ octopuses

☐ × ☐ = ☐

☐ octopuses

☐ × ☐ = ☐

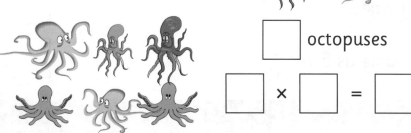

☐ octopuses

☐ × ☐ = ☐

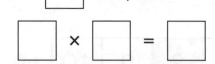

☐ octopuses

☐ × ☐ = ☐

Write the answers to the questions below.

1) A spider has eight legs. How many legs
are there on seven spiders?

☐

2) £80 is split equally between eight people.
How much money does each person get?

£ ☐

3) A hotel has eight floors. There are nine rooms on
each floor. How many rooms are there in total?

☐

4) A case holds eight bottles of water. How many
cases would you need for 64 bottles of water?

☐

Write the answers to the questions below.
See how fast you can do them all.

3	×	8	=	24		8	×	☐	=	80
☐	×	8	=	32		8	×	9	=	☐
☐	×	7	=	56		8	×	☐	=	32
8	×	☐	=	8		8	×	☐	=	48
9	×	8	=	☐		5	×	8	=	☐
☐	×	4	=	32		8	×	☐	=	72
2	×	8	=	☐		8	×	8	=	☐
8	×	☐	=	24		☐	×	3	=	24
8	×	10	=	☐		7	×	8	=	☐
6	×	☐	=	48		☐	×	6	=	48
8	×	5	=	☐		10	×	8	=	☐
☐	×	8	=	64		☐	×	2	=	16
9	×	☐	=	72		5	×	8	=	☐
☐	×	7	=	56		1	×	☐	=	8
4	×	8	=	☐		9	×	8	=	☐
☐	×	5	=	40		5	×	☐	=	40
6	×	☐	=	48		☐	×	8	=	56
8	×	9	=	☐		8	×	☐	=	64

27

NINE times table

Here is the nine times table: ⟶

The numbers in each answer to the nine times table add up to nine.

For example:
18
⇓ ⇓
1 + 8 = 9

1	×	9	=	9
2	×	9	=	18
3	×	9	=	27
4	×	9	=	36
5	×	9	=	45
6	×	9	=	54
7	×	9	=	63
8	×	9	=	72
9	×	9	=	81
10	×	9	=	90

Cover up the nine times table above.
Then fill in the blanks in the calculations below.

1	×	9	=	9		6	×	9	=	☐
☐	×	9	=	18		7	×	9	=	☐
☐	×	9	=	27		☐	×	9	=	72
4	×	9	=	☐		☐	×	9	=	81
5	×	9	=	☐		10	×	9	=	☐

Write the answers to the questions in the boxes.

How many nines make 18?   2

What is nine multiplied by seven?   ☐

What are five nines?   ☐

How many nines are the same as 81?   ☐

What is six multiplied by nine?   ☐

What is ten multiplied by nine?   ☐

How many eights make 72?   ☐

Five friends go shopping for some new T-shirts. Work out how much they each spend.

£9   Andrew buys four T-shirts.   £ 36

£10 Jade buys nine T-shirts.   £ ☐

£9   Sachin buys two T-shirts.   £ ☐

£9   Shanice buys eight T-shirts.   £ ☐

£6   Matt buys nine T-shirts.   £ ☐

NINE times table

Solve the calculations below. Each answer matches up with a letter. Use the letters to complete the words.

4 × 9   9 × 8   9 × 2   3 × 9   7 × 9   9 × 9   9 × 10   8 × 9   9 × 6

__ __   __ __   _E_   __ __   __ __   __ __   __ __   __ __   __ __

Answer	18	27	36	54	63	72	81	90
Letter	E	A	G	K	T	R	W	O

Colour in each part of the picture that has a multiple of nine.

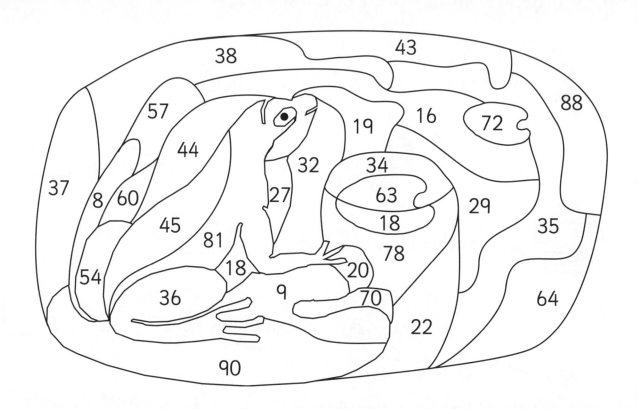

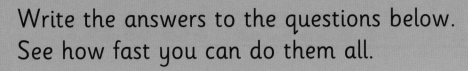

Write the answers to the questions below.
See how fast you can do them all.

9	×	1	=	9		10	×	9	=	☐
☐	×	9	=	72		9	×	☐	=	63
9	×	5	=	☐		9	×	3	=	☐
☐	×	9	=	54		9	×	☐	=	81
☐	×	7	=	63		☐	×	8	=	72
9	×	2	=	☐		7	×	☐	=	63
8	×	☐	=	72		4	×	☐	=	36
6	×	9	=	☐		9	×	9	=	☐
7	×	9	=	☐		5	×	9	=	☐
9	×	9	=	☐		☐	×	9	=	54
☐	×	9	=	27		3	×	9	=	☐
9	×	☐	=	72		9	×	☐	=	9
9	×	☐	=	36		☐	×	9	=	63
9	×	7	=	☐		8	×	9	=	☐
☐	×	6	=	54		9	×	☐	=	36
4	×	9	=	☐		☐	×	10	=	90
9	×	☐	=	18		9	×	☐	=	72
☐	×	9	=	63		☐	×	9	=	81

ELEVEN times table

Here is the eleven times table:

The multiples of eleven repeat the same number twice. Don't forget to add a zero for 110 though.

1	×	11	=	11
2	×	11	=	22
3	×	11	=	33
4	×	11	=	44
5	×	11	=	55
6	×	11	=	66
7	×	11	=	77
8	×	11	=	88
9	×	11	=	99
10	×	11	=	110

Cover up the eleven times table above.
Then fill in the blanks in the calculations below.

1	×	11	=	11	☐	×	11	=	66
☐	×	11	=	22	7	×	11	=	☐
3	×	11	=	☐	8	×	11	=	☐
☐	×	11	=	44	☐	×	11	=	99
☐	×	11	=	55	10	×	11	=	☐

Write the answers to the questions in the boxes.

How many elevens are the same as 44?   4

What are seven elevens?

What is two multiplied by eleven?

What is ten multiplied by eleven?

How many elevens make 33?

How many elevens are the same as 99?

How many elevens make 88?

What is five multiplied by eleven?

The calculator multiplies each number by eleven.
Fill in the missing numbers.

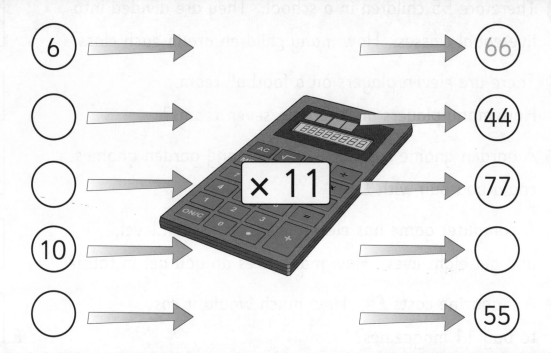

33

ELEVEN times table

A car is on a roundabout. It only drives on roads that are multiples of eleven. How many roads can the car drive on?

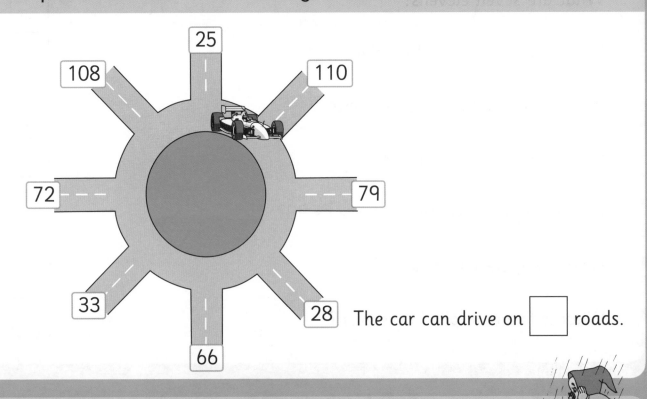

The car can drive on ☐ roads.

Write the answers to the questions below.

1. There are 55 children in a school. They are divided into five equal classes. How many children are in each class? ☐

2. There are eleven players on a football team. How many players are there on seven teams? ☐

3. A garden gnome costs £11. How many garden gnomes could you buy with £99? ☐

4. A computer game has eleven levels. On each level, you get eight lives. How many lives do you get in total? ☐

5. A magazine costs £4. How much would it cost to buy 11 magazines? £☐

Write the answers to the questions below.
See how fast you can do them all.

3 × 11 = 33			11 × ☐ = 88		
7 × 11 = ☐			☐ × 9 = 99		
4 × 11 = ☐			7 × ☐ = 77		
☐ × 1 = 11			4 × 11 = ☐		
11 × 6 = ☐			11 × ☐ = 33		
☐ × 4 = 44			9 × 11 = ☐		
8 × ☐ = 88			1 × ☐ = 11		
11 × 7 = ☐			11 × 10 = ☐		
9 × ☐ = 99			☐ × 11 = 88		
10 × ☐ = 110			11 × 6 = ☐		
2 × 11 = ☐			☐ × 7 = 77		
☐ × 9 = 99			11 × 8 = ☐		
5 × ☐ = 55			11 × ☐ = 44		
☐ × 11 = 66			1 × 11 = ☐		
9 × 11 = ☐			☐ × 11 = 110		
7 × 11 = ☐			11 × ☐ = 55		
☐ × 11 = 88			☐ × 11 = 99		
11 × ☐ = 22			6 × ☐ = 66		

TWELVE times table

Here is the twelve times table:

The answers to the twelve times table are double the answers to the six times table.

For example:
2 × 6 = 12
2 × 12 = 24

1	×	12	=	12
2	×	12	=	24
3	×	12	=	36
4	×	12	=	48
5	×	12	=	60
6	×	12	=	72
7	×	12	=	84
8	×	12	=	96
9	×	12	=	108
10	×	12	=	120

Cover up the twelve times table above.
Then fill in the blanks in the calculations below.

1	×	12	=	12	6	×	12	=	☐
☐	×	12	=	24	7	×	12	=	☐
☐	×	12	=	36	☐	×	12	=	96
4	×	12	=	☐	9	×	12	=	☐
☐	×	12	=	60	☐	×	12	=	120

Write the answers to the questions in the boxes.

What are four twelves? `48`

How many twelves are the same as 96? ☐

What is seven multiplied by twelve? ☐

What is three multiplied by twelve? ☐

How many twelves make 60? ☐

How many twelves are the same as 108? ☐

Doughnuts come in boxes of twelve.
How many doughnuts are in each set?

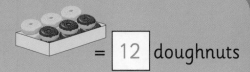 = `12` doughnuts

`2` boxes

`2` × `12` = `24`

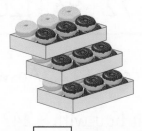

☐ boxes

☐ × ☐ = ☐

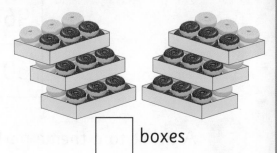

☐ boxes

☐ × ☐ = ☐

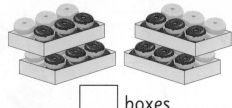

☐ boxes

☐ × ☐ = ☐

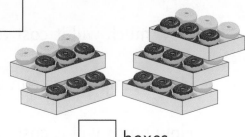

☐ boxes

☐ × ☐ = ☐

37

TWELVE times table

1 Circle the calculation below that would give the answer 84.

10 × 12	12 × 8	12 × 6
7 × 12	9 × 12	12 × 4

2 Draw a line to make a path from the start to the finish.
You can only go through the numbers in the twelve times table.

Start ⟹

48	24	40	8	77
32	36	98	46	92
108	12	104	62	80
96	88	110	16	34
60	72	84	120	24

⟹ Finish

3 A ticket to a theme park costs £12. Answer the questions below.

How many tickets can you buy with £24? ☐

How much will it cost to buy six tickets? £ ☐

How much will it cost to buy five tickets? £ ☐

How many tickets can you buy with £108? ☐

How much will it cost to buy ten tickets? £ ☐

How many tickets can you buy with £84? ☐

Write the answers to the questions below.
See how fast you can do them all.

3 × 12 = 36

□ × 12 = 96

12 × 9 = □

12 × □ = 48

12 × □ = 60

7 × 12 = □

□ × 12 = 120

12 × □ = 12

8 × □ = 96

□ × 12 = 84

12 × 7 = □

8 × □ = 96

12 × □ = 24

9 × 12 = □

□ × 12 = 108

6 × □ = 72

10 × 12 = □

12 × 4 = □

□ × 4 = 48

□ × 9 = 108

8 × □ = 96

12 × □ = 84

6 × 12 = □

12 × 8 = □

12 × □ = 12

3 × 12 = □

□ × 7 = 84

12 × □ = 72

1 × □ = 12

□ × 12 = 108

□ × 9 = 108

□ × 12 = 84

5 × 12 = □

12 × 2 = □

12 × □ = 72

4 × □ = 48

Mixed Questions

Multiply together the numbers that the arrow is pointing to.

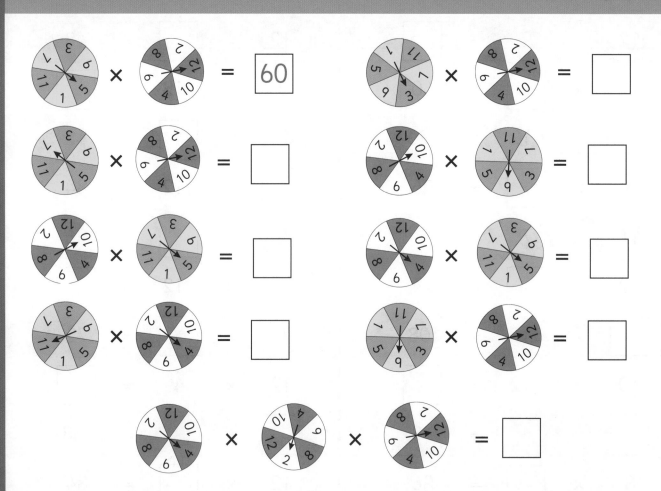

Draw lines to match each multiplication to its correct answer.

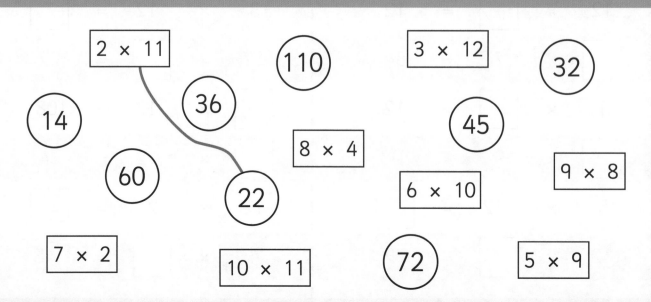

Write the answers to the questions in the boxes.

What are three sevens? `21`

What is nine multiplied by three? ☐

What is twelve multiplied by seven? ☐

How many threes make 33? ☐

How many elevens are the same as 55? ☐

What is seven multiplied by itself? ☐

What are ten twelves? ☐

Fill in the boxes to show how much it would cost to buy the following pets in a pet shop.

goldfish £4   guinea pig £7   rabbit £9   cat £12

2 goldfish £ `8`   7 guinea pigs £ ☐

4 guinea pigs £ ☐   5 cats £ ☐

6 goldfish £ ☐   11 goldfish £ ☐

4 cats £ ☐   4 rabbits £ ☐

6 rabbits £ ☐   9 guinea pigs £ ☐

Mixed Questions

Complete the multiplication grid.

×	1	2	3	4	5	6	7	8	9	10
1	1					6				
2		4					14			
3			9	12						30
4					20				36	
5		10					35			
6	6									60
7			21					56		
8				32		48				
9	9						63			
10			30						90	
11		22						88		
12					60	72				

Underline the calculation that equals the number in the circle.

(36) ➡ 6 × 7   7 × 5   <u>4 × 9</u>   10 × 4

(50) ➡ 9 × 5   8 × 6   5 × 10   6 × 10

(64) ➡ 12 × 5   8 × 8   10 × 6   7 × 9

(96) ➡ 7 × 12   10 × 9   12 × 9   12 × 8

Write the answers to the questions below.
See how fast you can do them all.

$\boxed{7}$	×	2	=	14		$\boxed{}$	×	9	=	108
11	×	$\boxed{}$	=	77		10	×	$\boxed{}$	=	40
$\boxed{}$	×	6	=	30		7	×	12	=	$\boxed{}$
10	×	2	=	$\boxed{}$		3	×	$\boxed{}$	=	3
7	×	$\boxed{}$	=	21		$\boxed{}$	×	2	=	18
$\boxed{}$	×	12	=	108		10	×	$\boxed{}$	=	120
3	×	5	=	$\boxed{}$		9	×	5	=	$\boxed{}$
$\boxed{}$	×	7	=	70		6	×	$\boxed{}$	=	66
8	×	$\boxed{}$	=	96		12	×	4	=	$\boxed{}$
5	×	12	=	$\boxed{}$		$\boxed{}$	×	3	=	33
2	×	$\boxed{}$	=	12		9	×	$\boxed{}$	=	63
$\boxed{}$	×	8	=	56		7	×	6	=	$\boxed{}$
6	×	9	=	$\boxed{}$		11	×	8	=	$\boxed{}$
3	×	$\boxed{}$	=	33		8	×	$\boxed{}$	=	96
2	×	$\boxed{}$	=	16		$\boxed{}$	×	4	=	28
$\boxed{}$	×	4	=	36		$\boxed{}$	×	9	=	99
12	×	$\boxed{}$	=	36		6	×	6	=	$\boxed{}$
4	×	4	=	$\boxed{}$		5	×	$\boxed{}$	=	20

All the times tables

One times table

$1 \times 1 = 1$
$2 \times 1 = 2$
$3 \times 1 = 3$
$4 \times 1 = 4$
$5 \times 1 = 5$
$6 \times 1 = 6$
$7 \times 1 = 7$
$8 \times 1 = 8$
$9 \times 1 = 9$
$10 \times 1 = 10$

Two times table

$1 \times 2 = 2$
$2 \times 2 = 4$
$3 \times 2 = 6$
$4 \times 2 = 8$
$5 \times 2 = 10$
$6 \times 2 = 12$
$7 \times 2 = 14$
$8 \times 2 = 16$
$9 \times 2 = 18$
$10 \times 2 = 20$

Three times table

$1 \times 3 = 3$
$2 \times 3 = 6$
$3 \times 3 = 9$
$4 \times 3 = 12$
$5 \times 3 = 15$
$6 \times 3 = 18$
$7 \times 3 = 21$
$8 \times 3 = 24$
$9 \times 3 = 27$
$10 \times 3 = 30$

Four times table

$1 \times 4 = 4$
$2 \times 4 = 8$
$3 \times 4 = 12$
$4 \times 4 = 16$
$5 \times 4 = 20$
$6 \times 4 = 24$
$7 \times 4 = 28$
$8 \times 4 = 32$
$9 \times 4 = 36$
$10 \times 4 = 40$

Five times table

$1 \times 5 = 5$
$2 \times 5 = 10$
$3 \times 5 = 15$
$4 \times 5 = 20$
$5 \times 5 = 25$
$6 \times 5 = 30$
$7 \times 5 = 35$
$8 \times 5 = 40$
$9 \times 5 = 45$
$10 \times 5 = 50$

Six times table

$1 \times 6 = 6$
$2 \times 6 = 12$
$3 \times 6 = 18$
$4 \times 6 = 24$
$5 \times 6 = 30$
$6 \times 6 = 36$
$7 \times 6 = 42$
$8 \times 6 = 48$
$9 \times 6 = 54$
$10 \times 6 = 60$

Seven times table

$1 \times 7 = 7$
$2 \times 7 = 14$
$3 \times 7 = 21$
$4 \times 7 = 28$
$5 \times 7 = 35$
$6 \times 7 = 42$
$7 \times 7 = 49$
$8 \times 7 = 56$
$9 \times 7 = 63$
$10 \times 7 = 70$

Eight times table

$1 \times 8 = 8$
$2 \times 8 = 16$
$3 \times 8 = 24$
$4 \times 8 = 32$
$5 \times 8 = 40$
$6 \times 8 = 48$
$7 \times 8 = 56$
$8 \times 8 = 64$
$9 \times 8 = 72$
$10 \times 8 = 80$

Nine times table

$1 \times 9 = 9$
$2 \times 9 = 18$
$3 \times 9 = 27$
$4 \times 9 = 36$
$5 \times 9 = 45$
$6 \times 9 = 54$
$7 \times 9 = 63$
$8 \times 9 = 72$
$9 \times 9 = 81$
$10 \times 9 = 90$

Ten times table

$1 \times 10 = 10$
$2 \times 10 = 20$
$3 \times 10 = 30$
$4 \times 10 = 40$
$5 \times 10 = 50$
$6 \times 10 = 60$
$7 \times 10 = 70$
$8 \times 10 = 80$
$9 \times 10 = 90$
$10 \times 10 = 100$

Eleven times table

$1 \times 11 = 11$
$2 \times 11 = 22$
$3 \times 11 = 33$
$4 \times 11 = 44$
$5 \times 11 = 55$
$6 \times 11 = 66$
$7 \times 11 = 77$
$8 \times 11 = 88$
$9 \times 11 = 99$
$10 \times 11 = 110$

Twelve times table

$1 \times 12 = 12$
$2 \times 12 = 24$
$3 \times 12 = 36$
$4 \times 12 = 48$
$5 \times 12 = 60$
$6 \times 12 = 72$
$7 \times 12 = 84$
$8 \times 12 = 96$
$9 \times 12 = 108$
$10 \times 12 = 120$

MPTT21